PHOENIX SOCIETY FOR BURN SURVIVORS

HOW TO USE THIS BOOK

Sara's STEPS was developed by Phoenix Society for Burn Survivors to help preschool and elementary school-age burn survivors, their siblings, and children of burn survivors.

Using this book as a guide, you can help your child develop skills to feel more confident talking about their own or their loved one's burn injury in social situations. Your child will learn how to manage staring, respond to comments from other children, and answer questions from others.

At the end of the book, you'll find further activities for any caring adult to help children learn and practice these skills. Use this material to start conversations about burn injuries and other visible differences.

This book uses several resources taught by Phoenix Society that have been adapted for children. For adult resources on social skills and supporting a burn-injured loved one, visit www.phoenix-society.org.

CONTRIBUTORS

Michelle Lauren Anderson, MBA, MS
Jessica Irven, MS, LRT/CTRS, CCLS, CTP-C
Barbara Kammerer Quayle, MA
Megan Tinny, PT, DPT
Pam Peterson, RN, BSN

Phoenix Society for Burn Survivors

525 Ottawa Ave NW | Grand Rapids, MI 40503 | 1.800.888.BURN | info@phoenix-society.org

SARA'S
STEPS

WRITTEN BY NIKI AVERTON + NICOLE PERRY
ILLUSTRATED BY LYN STONE

One day, Sara and her dad were in a car crash.
They were rushed to the hospital in an ambulance
and had to stay for a long, long time.

Sara and her dad were both burned in the accident.
Sara had scars on her face and her body, and she
still had to wear special gloves called pressure
garments to help her hands heal.

When it was finally time for Sara to go back to school, she knew
she should feel happy—but all she felt was NERVOUS.

"Can I be home-schooled from now on?" Sara asked her mom.

"No, sweetie," said Mom. "It's important to get back to the things you did before the accident. I know you will do great!"

"Don't worry," added Sara's brother, Daniel. "I'll be right there with you."

Sara just wanted to hide under the bed.

In the morning, Sara started to feel excited about seeing her friends— but she still felt pretty nervous.

What if they didn't want to be her friends anymore?

What if they whispered or gave her funny looks?

What if they asked what happened?

When they got to school, Sara didn't want to go inside.

"It's going to be okay," Daniel said. "Let's go in together."

Inside, Sara kept her head down. Daniel walked her all the way to her class.

But then Sara's teacher started class by telling everyone to give Sara a big welcome back.

"Sara was in an accident," he said. "She had to go to the hospital, but she's doing better now and we're so happy she's back with our class!"

Everyone smiled and clapped.

Maybe this wouldn't be so bad!

At lunchtime, everyone hurried out of the classroom.
Suddenly, Sara was in the middle of a crowded hall.
It seemed like everyone was whispering.

"What happened to that girl?"

"What's wrong with your face?"

"What's on your hand?"

"Were you burned in a fire?"

Sara couldn't take it anymore. She pushed her way through
the crowd and locked herself in a bathroom stall to cry.

After school, Mom had a big plate of cookies
waiting on the table, but Sara and Daniel were
too upset for snacks.

When Dad got home, he plopped down on the couch next to Daniel.

"What happened at school today, kids?" asked Dad.

"Everyone stared at her," Daniel burst out.

Sara nodded. "They wouldn't stop asking me questions."

"They even asked *me* questions," said Daniel. "I didn't know what to say."

Sara sniffled. "I *never* want to go back to school."

"Not so fast," said Dad, starting to smile. "I think I know something that can help. When I was in the hospital, they taught me a tool from Phoenix Society for Burn Survivors. It helped me feel brave and know what to say. It's called..."

STEPS

S is for
SELF TALK

Tell yourself nice things to help you feel brave!

T is for
TONE OF VOICE

Talk friendly, happy, and excited!

E is for
EYE CONTACT
Look 'em in the eye!

P is for
POSTURE
Stand up straight!

S is for
SMILE
Give a warm and friendly smile!

"It can also help to **Rehearse Your Response**," Dad said. "When people ask you questions, have a quick response ready. Try including these three parts:

1. Say what happened.

2. Describe how you're doing now.

3. End the conversation.

"Want to hear mine?" said Dad.

"Yeah!" shouted Sara and Daniel.

Dad used his STEPS. He put on a big smile,
stood up straight, and looked them in the eye.

"I was burned in a car accident.

I'm doing fine now.

Thank you for asking."

On the way to the bus stop the next morning, Sara and Daniel practiced their STEPS and their Rehearsed Responses.

Sara started with **self-talk**.

I'm brave.

I'm strong.

I can do anything!

Then she prepared her nicest **tone of voice** and made **eye contact** with Daniel.

"Hi Daniel!"

"Hi Sara," Daniel said. Then he pretended to stare at her scars. "What happened to your face?"

Sara remembered her **posture** and stood up straight and tall.

She gave her biggest **smile**.

"I was burned in a car accident. I'm doing great now! Thanks for asking."

"Nice job!" said Daniel.

When they got to school, everyone stared at first, but Sara and Daniel knew just what to do.

They walked down the hallway like they were happy to be there, standing up straight and looking everyone in the eyes.

Whenever anyone asked a question, they used their Rehearsed Responses.

"I was burned in a car accident," Sara said to one curious boy.
"I'm doing great now. That's all I want to say about it right now."

"My sister was burned in a car accident," Daniel told his friend.
"She is so brave and now she's doing well! Thanks for asking."

They kept walking, smiling at everyone they saw. By the time they got to their classrooms, everyone was smiling back.

Sara and Daniel keep using STEPS and rehearsed responses to feel comfortable with all kinds of people and places.

They start with **self-talk**...

I'm brave...

I'm strong...

I can do anything!

THE END

HELPING YOUR PRESCHOOLER (3-6)
LEARN AND MASTER SOCIAL SKILLS

WHAT WE KNOW ABOUT PRESCHOOLERS

- They start to become more independent and comfortable away from parents.

- They ask a lot of questions, especially "why?"

- Younger preschoolers have a hard time grasping the permanence of their burn injury and may frequently ask when it will go away.

- They have relatively short attention spans.

- Play is central to this age, and they enjoy both imaginative and pretend play.

- They often communicate through play since their language is limited.

- They can follow simple rules/instructions and always want to win at games.

- Trauma can come out in other ways, such as difficulty focusing, more frequent tantrums, and regression (such as bedwetting).

SUPPORTING YOUR PRESCHOOLER

- Provide structure and routines for your child. This creates a safe, predictable environment.

- Set limits and be consistent when disciplining your child. If you tell them "no," be sure to explain what they should be doing instead.

- Find opportunities for your child to have social interactions or play groups with peers. This helps them learn the value of friendship, cooperation, and sharing.

- Give opportunities for your child to have control when possible. Give your child a limited number of appropriate choices: "Do you want to take your medicine in a medicine cup or syringe?"

- Help your child problem solve when they are upset. Provide suggestions or guidance and allow your child to help create the solution.

- Avoid talking down to your child by using "baby talk" – use "grown up" words to support language development and skills.

- Encourage your child's independence and provide praise with successes.

- Know that even young children can benefit from therapeutic programs and therapists' support.

TEACHING SOCIAL SKILLS TO YOUR PRESCHOOLER

- Children learn through repetition and practice. Provide opportunities for your child to practice social skills in a safe and supported environment, such as during playtime.

- Provide basic, simple explanations of each of the five STEPS (self-talk, tone of voice, eye contact, posture, smile) in social skills. Use the *Sara's STEPS* book and bookmark as a tool for learning and examples of appropriate language.

  - Since preschoolers have a short attention span, focus on learning the five steps one at a time. For instance, practice the smile step one day, making good eye contact another day, etc.

  - Preschoolers may have a hard time grasping the concept of self-talk. Teach this concept by focusing on helping children identify positive aspects about themselves. Help your child develop a short, repetitive mantra of their positive characteristics. For example, "I am kind, smart and loved."

- Begin to help your child develop their rehearsed response. Use repetition to help your child memorize it.

- Model appropriate social skills tools for your child. Your child will be looking to you for appropriate ways to respond, so it is crucial to also demonstrate these skills yourself.

- Make it fun! Use art activities or imaginary/ dramatic play with stuffed animals, dolls, or action figures to talk about STEPS and rehearsed responses.

  - Observe your child's play. They may be expressing concerns or feelings by projecting them onto toys during play.

- Provide opportunities for your child to be around other burn survivors to help normalize the experience and have role models.

ACTIVITY #1
BE A MOVIE STAR

GOALS
This age-appropriate activity provides a fun, interactive, and supportive way to learn and practice social skills.

MATERIALS NEEDED
- *Sara's STEPS* book
- STEPS/RYR cards or bookmarks
- "Dress up"/imaginary play accessories
- Photo booth props such as a microphone or wand
- Markers and paper
- Camera (real or make-believe)

ACTIVITY
Read *Sara's STEPS* with your child. Help your child develop a rehearsed response and learn the five STEPS. Using five pieces of paper, write one of the five STEPS (self-talk, tone of voice, eye contact, posture, smile) on each.

Create a pretend runway or red-carpet scene. Have your child pick one of the steps from the five papers and then take turns practicing that step by using the props to walk down the runway.

You will play the role of the media/paparazzi, so ask your child questions and take real or pretend photos as your child struts their stuff down the runway. Sample questions you can ask:

- What is something you love about yourself?
- Tell me about your burn injury? / What happened to your sibling?
- What is your favorite thing to do for fun?

Praise your child throughout the exercise and point out specific things they did really well.

ACTIVITY #2
"ME MOBILES"

GOALS
This activity focuses on the "self-talk" step and assists your child in developing a positive sense of self by allowing your child to identify positive characteristics about themself.

MATERIALS NEEDED
- Plastic hanger
- Photo of your child
- Yarn/ribbon/string
- Scissors
- Crayons/markers, child-friendly magazines, stickers
- Hole punch
- Glue sticks
- Index cards cut into various shapes (circles, stars, squares, hearts, etc.)

ACTIVITY
Have your child glue the photo to the top of the hanger. Then have your child select five of the pre-cut shapes to decorate. Ask your child to tell you their five favorite things about themself. Each of the cut-out shapes will be decorated to represent these five things.

Your child can decorate the cutouts using markers/crayons, images from the magazines, stickers, or any other collage style items you have laying around the house. Creativity encouraged!

Once decorated, use the hole punch to place a hole in each of the decorated shapes. Cut five strings/ribbons into various lengths. Tie one end of each of the strings to the hanger and the other ends to the decorated shape.

Have your child share the completed mobile with another friend or family member.

HELPING YOUR SCHOOL-AGE CHILD (7-12)
LEARN AND MASTER SOCIAL SKILLS

WHAT WE KNOW ABOUT SCHOOL-AGE CHILDREN

- They need boundaries but also need to feel a sense of control. Acting out may be your child's way to try to control what they can.

- They think literally and their beliefs are often focused on facts.

- Their problem-solving and rational thinking abilities are improving.

- They seek and take high value in peer approval – peers are very important to them.

- They may show jealousy of siblings and peers.

- They have developed a sense of body image and are usually modest about their body.

- They have a need to feel successful and are encouraged by praise.

- They enjoy friendly competition and games.

SUPPORTING YOUR SCHOOL-AGE CHILD

- Encourage your child to talk with you about their concerns or emotions without fear of punishment.

- Set fitting expectations and consistently enforce them with appropriate consequences. Also allow your child control when appropriate, but maintain limits.

- Teach your child how to cope with frustration without losing self-esteem. Normalize setbacks by sharing your past failures and demonstrating how you've moved on or grown from the experiences.

- Set your child up for success by helping them choose activities appropriate for their abilities.

- Become aware of problems your child may keep from you by maintaining close communication with their teachers, school staff, and parents of their friends.

- Monitor your child's internet and social media usage. Note their search history or any cyberbullying.

- Provide frequent praise and compliments on your child's accomplishments.

TEACHING SOCIAL SKILLS TO YOUR SCHOOL-AGE CHILD

- Provide basic, simple explanations of each of the five STEPS (self-talk, tone of voice, eye contact, posture, smile) in social skills. Use the *Sara's STEPS* book and bookmark for examples of appropriate language.

  - Help your child master each step individually first.

  - Reinforce the importance of positive self-talk. It is challenging to bring your best self to a social situation if you have negative thoughts running through your mind.

- Help your child develop their rehearsed response and write it out on an index card so they can keep it handy until it's memorized.

- Allow your child to express their discomfort and craft a statement that says, "I don't want to talk about this, thanks for understanding."

- Give examples your child can relate to by sharing times you've had positive social experiences because you used social skills.

- Allow your child to learn with other peers when possible. If your child has a supportive best friend, also teach social skills to them.

- Model appropriate social skills tools. Your child will be looking to you for appropriate ways to respond, so it is crucial to demonstrate these skills yourself.

- Children learn through repetition and practice. Provide opportunities for your child to practice these skills in a safe and supported environment.

- Provide praise when you notice proper use of social skills. For example:

  - "You made great eye contact when you were talking to the boy at the park."

  - "You were walking with great posture in the grocery story today. It made you look very confident."

- Make it fun – use role play, art, scenarios and examples to engage all learning styles.

- Normalize your child's experiences by getting them involved in programs such as Phoenix World Burn Congress or burn camps.

ACTIVITY #1
SOCIAL SKILLS SCAVENGER HUNT

GOALS
This activity provides a fun and supportive way to learn and practice social skills.

MATERIALS NEEDED
- *Sara's STEPS* book
- STEPS/RYR cards or bookmarks
- Scavenger Hunt check-off list (included below)
- Stickers

ACTIVITY
Read *Sara's STEPS* with your child. Help your child develop a rehearsed response and learn the five social skills STEPS. Once you have had a chance to practice, take your child on a Scavenger Hunt. Go to places you know you'll find other people – the grocery store, library, local park, etc. Practice each skill on the scavenger hunt list below, marking them with a sticker once they are completed.

After the scavenger hunt, spend time talking with your child about the experience. How did people respond when you used your skills? How did they respond when you did not use your skill?

SCAVENGER HUNT CHECK-OFF
- ☐ If you notice someone staring, make eye contact and say "hi."
- ☐ Smile at three people you see on the scavenger hunt. Pay attention to their reactions.
- ☐ Introduce yourself to someone wearing a hat. Say something positive to them about their outfit, such as "nice hat!"
- ☐ If someone asks about your burn injury, use your rehearsed response to reply.
- ☐ Start a conversation with a stranger.
- ☐ Focus on having good posture and making eye contact when walking by someone. Then practice having poor posture and not making eye contact when you walk by someone else. Notice how you feel with both postures.

ACTIVITY #2
SELF PORTRAITS: INSIDE + OUT

GOALS
This activity focuses on the "self-talk" step and provides an opportunity for self-expression, identifying positive and negative thoughts, and includes an exercise for getting rid of the negative thoughts and reinforcing positive ones.

MATERIALS NEEDED
- Four sheets of white copy paper
- Writing utensil (pen/pencil)
- Colored crayons or markers
- Black crayon or marker
- Index Cards

ACTIVITY
Provide your child with two pieces off white paper and keep two for yourself. Using one of the pieces of paper, draw yourselves in black and white. Using the second piece of paper, draw yourselves using colored crayons/makers.

On the black and white image, write any negative thoughts or feelings you have of yourselves. (These are the thoughts holding you back from achieving a positive self-image.) On the colorful drawing, write the positive thoughts and feelings you have of yourselves that promote positive self-esteem.

Once you have each completed writing out your individual positive and negative thoughts, share them with each other. After you've had a chance to share and talk about the feelings, take the black and white page, crinkle it up, and throw it in the garbage. Then pick three positive thoughts/feelings from the colorful page and write them on your index card.

Keep this index card in your pocket, and whenever you find yourself thinking about those negative feelings, pull out the index card and say those three positive thoughts out loud.

Made in the USA
Monee, IL
14 March 2024

55005864R00019